TRINITY
COLLEGE LONDON

MOSAICS

Flute

Book 1

65 solo pieces
by Mike Mower

Introduction

This collection of graded pieces for the flute was written with the idea of entertaining the player and listener with a variety of styles, both old and modern. Often with a quirky element, each piece is intended to stand on its own as a short concert piece rather than a study: I had the idea that perhaps a selection of a few of the pieces chosen by the performer could be played together as a concert performance suite.

In my playing and writing career, starting as a classically trained musician, I subsequently became involved with many different musical styles from around the world and with different genres such as jazz, rock and pop; I've incorporated some of these styles into this book.

The pieces are organised in order of difficulty so the player can easily map his or her progress. Book 1 ranges from beginner to approximately Grade 5 standard, and Book 2 pieces are from Grade 6 to Grade 8 standard. The more advanced pieces are suitable for inclusion in the solo performance of GCSE, A Level and International Baccalaureate examinations.

To pre-empt some possible questions:

▶ Double barlines indicate the beginning of a new section of the piece
▶ Accidentals apply only to their octave
▶ In sections without barlines, accidentals apply only to their beamed group
▶ The swing element in jazz is 'tripletty' at slow tempos, but lessens and becomes straighter as the tempo increases
▶ *flz.* = fluttertonguing (preferred, but optional).

I hope you have as much enjoyment playing these pieces as I have had writing them!

Mike Mower

Published by
Trinity College London

Registered Office:
89 Albert Embankment
London SE1 7TP UK

T +44 (0)20 7820 6100
F +44 (0)20 7820 6161
E music@trinitycollege.co.uk
www.trinitycollege.co.uk

Registered in the UK
Company no. 02683033
Charity no. 1014792

Printed in England by Halstan, Amersham, Bucks.

Contents

1. Out for the Count

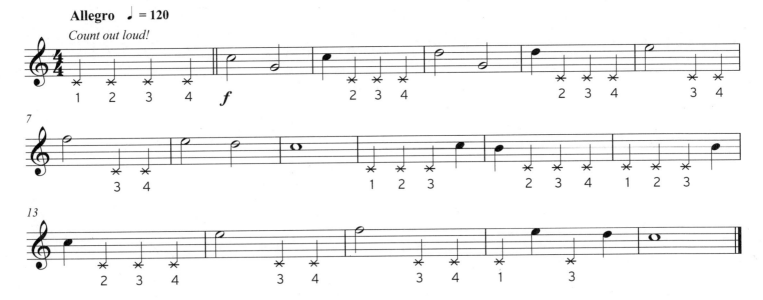

2. A Recurring Theme

3. All Face the Middle

4. Easy Day Ahead

5. Three for the Count

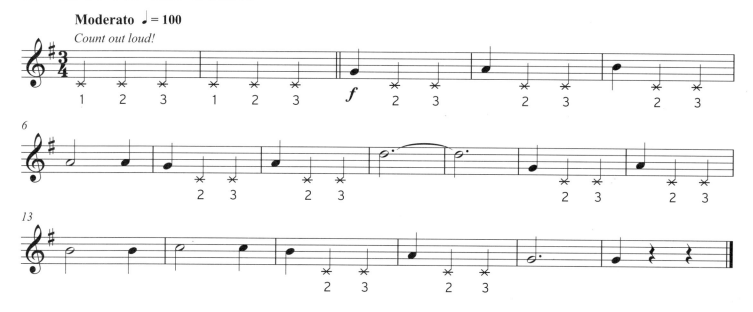

6. Tapperboard

7. Effscale

8. Geescale

9. Bad King Carol

10. Long Short

11. Orange Peal

12. Eee by Gum

13. Funky Pheasant

14. Mini Miner

15. That Note Again

16. Spambusters March

17. Whisty

18. A Recurring Theme (1)

19. A Shaky Start

20. Morning Yawning

21. Jigglet Gravy

22. Bassalt 'n' Vinegar

23. March of the Modems

24. Winter Sunset

25. Cucumber Wallbanger

26. Polkamon

27. The Spy

28. Lotus Pocus

29. A Recurring Theme (2)

30. Crayfish Bake

31. Beefy

32. Jig-Jag

33. Just a Minuet

34. Creeping up on Grandma

Flutter tonguing is optional.

35. Marchetto

36. Bloop

37. March Pear

38. The Retro Waltz

One-in-a-bar Waltz ♩ = 148

39. A Recurring Theme (3)

40. Tudor Mood

41. Pentawaltz

42. Nice and Smooth

43. The Inebriated Hornpipe

44. A Wee Dram

Highland March ♩ = 116

45. Ballade

46. A Country Walk

26

47. Cha-Cha Charlie

48. The Funky Monk

49. Chewing Gum Underfoot

50. Teatime

51. Staccatango

52. A Recurring Theme (4)

53. Rumba of the Bailey

54. Strong but Strident

55. B minor Mess

56. Gavotte Spot

57. Pinewood Carry-on

Flutter tonguing is optional.

58. Symbiosis

59. A flat Majorette

60. Fantasy in F♯ minor

61. Jeux sans Pommes

62. Four Before B

One-in-a-bar waltz ♩. = 56

63. My Dad's an Accountant

64. Three Flat Mice

65. A Recurring Theme (5)